C000242520

WHAT IF?

WHAT IF?

A Chronicle of What Might Have Been

edited and illustrated by
ANNIE WEST

NEW ISLAND

Nostradamus considers his next prediction

LIVE
Romantic nights with
ALBERT EINSTEIN
and his Orchestra
SOLD OUT

What if Einstein hadn't given up the day-job?

Dr David Robert Grimes

Historians call 1905 Albert Einstein's *annus mirabilis* – his miracle year. The young physicist, to his immense frustration, had been unable to find teaching positions, and had instead taken up employment as a patent clerk in Switzerland. Whilst there, he undertook perhaps the most profound moonlighting in history, publishing several works with staggering implications for how we view the universe. His work on the photoelectric effect became the cornerstone of quantum mechanics, eventually winning him a Nobel Prize. His special theory of relativity introduced the counter-intuitive notion that while measurements of time and space are different for observers moving at varying speeds, the speed of light remains constant. From this, he showed mass and energy are equivalent, giving us the most famously elegant equation in the world: $E = mc^2$. Coaxed back into academia, his later general theory of relativity explained gravity as the warping of space-time by massive objects. This prediction, when validated, made him the archetypical physicist we know today.

Yet, had Einstein in 1905 pursed his other passions, things might have been very different – he was, for example, an avid and capable violinist. After hearing him play, a 1920's music critic, evidently unaware that his celebrity derived from something other than musical prowess, remarked, 'Einstein's playing is excellent, but he does not deserve his world fame; there are many others just as good.' What if Einstein opted to abandon research and pursue the life of a violinist, or remain strictly clerical? What would have transpired had he decided that he was quite happy at the patent office, without all the hassle of superfluous calculation and mental exertion?

Maybe now we'd be praising of Einstein the violinist rather than the physicist – but we'd be listening to him on tape. Without his insight into the phenomenon of stimulated emission, the laser would never have been invented, rendering CDs and DVDs non-existent. Not only would we be forced to endure scratchy tapes on long journeys, we'd be perpetually lost too – relativity dictates that the clocks we use aboard satellites for our GPS systems tick slower than clocks on Earth. General relativity further predicts clocks closer to a massive object, like Earth, tick slower than those in orbit. When these effects are considered, the discrepancy between clocks on Earth and clocks in space is about thirty-eight microseconds. This tiny error perpetuates quickly – without relativity, it would throw us out by ten kilometres daily. That's the difference between your map telling you that your house is in Dublin one day and Glasgow a month later.

Nor would we be able to complain about this on our phones; the humble semi-conductor relies on quantum principles, which would be foggy had Einstein decided his passion was patents, not physics. Light-emitting diodes and charged coupled devices would cease to exist, relegating mobile phones, modern cameras and digital devices to the realm of science fiction. Even medicine would be altered, as everything from MRI and PET to particle therapy owes its existence, in part at least, to the flamboyantly coiffured physicist.

In an alternative past, Einstein of 1905 might have devoted himself entirely to his day-job, ceasing his now legendary thought experiments. There's no doubt a fully focused Einstein would have made an exemplary patent clerk, but the world might be the darker for it – something worth remembering the next time you're berated for daydreaming at work!

'Well I see Setanta has arrived'

What if the weather had been worse?
Tom Foley

Ben Franklin walked out of his house on a stormy, wet afternoon in May, 1752, despite his wife's concerns. Deborah shook her head. 'Why is it so important to fly a kite today?'

'Lost time is never found again,' he replied thoughtfully.

'Well, I don't think it's wise,' she said.

After thinking a moment, Ben mumbled back, 'Tell me and I forget, teach me and I remember, involve me and I learn.'

Ben flew his kite and showed that sparks did fly between his hand and the key hung on a wet string attached to his kite, proving that storm clouds are electrically charged. But what if the weather had been worse and Mr Franklin had been killed? The weather was indeed worse a month later in Russia when Professor George Wilhelm Richman tried the same thing and was electrocuted. Several other experimenters followed Professor Wilhelm to their graves in the months after.

Had the clouds been a little more charged with electricity, Ben might have demonstrated the lightning rod a little earlier than planned, missing the opportunity to invent it later. The Continental Congress wouldn't have needed an eminence to sort out a final draft of the US Constitution. Ben wouldn't have been in Paris to convince the French to pitch in on the side of the American colonies. The revolutionary war might never have happened, or been lost. The United States of the UK? Viceroy Obama? Lord Mayor Bloomberg? Celebrities with titles? That definitely would have put some class and glitter on the place. Might have saved some money too. The war of 1812 could also have been skipped.

But it didn't happen. The Americans won their independence, have a constitution, wear bifocals, heat their homes with Franklin stoves, and have a not-so-pretty face on the $100 bill. Ben Franklin lived a long, happy life and went on to explain many useful things in addition to electricity, including the fact that wine is constant proof that God loves us and loves to see us happy.

After years at sea, Columbus finally discovers The New World

TAYTO

From the diary of Captain Robert Falcon Scott

Charlie Connelly

17 January, 1912

And so, after years of meticulous preparation, months at sea, and weeks of exhausting trekking, we are beaten. On arrival we found a flag already planted, here at the place we had coveted for so long, this godforsaken South Pole.

Our dreams of glory, of earning immortality for our names, are all gone. Amundsen bested us.

We fell to our knees. I reminded the men that this was a time for dignity and stoicism, for reflecting upon the enormity of our achievement, and for recognising Amundsen's feat in being the first man to reach the South Pole, the prick.

Then, from behind us, a voice.

'Jaysus, lads,' it said. 'Will yiz not come inside, it's feckin' borassic out here.'

I looked round, stunned, and saw a man trying to light a cigarette, hands cupped over his lighter. He shook it and called it a 'bollix' before flinging it into the snow and addressing us again.

'One of you boys wouldn't have a light, would ya?'

After procuring a match, he led us around a nearby ridge of snow to an extraordinary sight: a public house! Light spilled through steamed-up windows and sounds of laughter and conversation could be heard within. Our guide pushed the door open and ushered us inside, announcing, 'Gents, welcome to JJ Murphy's, known as Frosty Jack's.'

We stared open-mouthed at the scene. Elderly men sat on stools at the bar nursing pints of stout, squinting at the racing pages. A small child ran past me, spilling crumbs from a brightly coloured packet emblazoned 'Tayto'. Two German backpackers leafed through the jukebox catalogue.

We took a table near the fire, whereupon a young woman arrived and set down five pints of creamy stout from a tray, saying, 'There ye are, lads, you look like you need these, all right.' After exchanging uncertain glances, we raised the drinks to our lips, only to be stopped dead by a shout.

'No! Not yet, boys, let them settle first.'

The voice came from the other side of the fireplace, and there sat a man clad from head to foot in furs. Who else could it be but Amundsen, the prick.

He walked over, pulled up a low stool, looked conspiratorially from side to side and addressed us in a low voice.

'Now, gentlemen,' he began. 'Our expeditions have cost us a lot in terms of time and money. If it gets out that not only did the Irish get here first, but that they also opened a pub, we'll all be laughing stocks. I propose we collude on our accounts, confirming that I arrived before you but not mentioning this whole Frosty Jack's thing.'

It was clear we had little choice – being second to the Pole was bad enough, third was simply too much to bear. We nodded.

He stood up and held out his hand.

'No hard feelings, Captain Scott.'

We shook. He nodded and turned to go before pausing and looking back at us.

'By the way, what kept you?' he smiled. The prick.

Isaac Newton runs home to write down the Theory of Gravity

ACME
WASHING UP LIQUID
KILLS 99.9% of GERMS
ANTIBACTERIAL

What if Alexander Fleming had washed up?
Dr Dean Burnett

One of the most important discoveries in the history of medicine was a complete accident. Alexander Fleming was a brilliant scientist, but known to be very untidy, and left some bacteria cultures to grow in his filthy lab while he went on holiday. He returned to find some of his dishes had mould growing on them. Somehow, the mould utterly killed the bacteria around it, and from this fluke discovery came penicillin, and all subsequent antibiotics.

But, what if Fleming had been, like most people, just a bit more clean and hygienic? And yet, if he hadn't been as blasé about hygiene as he was, the whole of the human race would look different right now, and be arguably much worse off.

Without Fleming's filth-based fluke, who knows how long it would have taken for antibiotics to be discovered, assuming they would be at all? And while antibiotics only treat a limited range of ailments, many of these are very serious, like pneumonia and bronchitis. Think of the millions of people over the decades who have been cured of these illnesses by antibiotics and then … take them out of the picture. What would the world be like?

And that's just humans. Antibiotics are heavily used in farm animals too, so even our food supply would be severely changed.

And you think we as a society are cleanliness-obsessed now, then imagine a world where we know about all the common diseases and infections but there's nothing we can do about them. We might all be wandering around in scuba suits or mobile bubbles by now.

Think of that next time someone nags you to do the washing-up. You could be harming all of humanity by doing so.

This is what happens when you call them 'Monster Meetings'

Last Will & Testament
of Mrs. Maria Wood

To Katherine & William
Thanks for waiting
so long but I left it all
to your cousins.
Warmest wishes
Aunt Ben

If only she'd had the money...

Mary Kenny

Charles Stewart Parnell, 'The Uncrowned King of Ireland', is seen as the last political leader who might have brought about an independent Ireland, which would also have been a united Ireland. He was a brilliant parliamentary leader who championed the rights of the Irish peasant and affirmed Ireland's nationhood, despite also identifying as a Protestant (though privately he may not have been a religious believer). He might have pulled off the feat of bringing the Ulster Unionists into an independent Ireland.

But, as everyone knows, Parnell's career was ruined when it became publicly known, in 1890, that the woman he loved and lived with, Katharine O'Shea, was already married to Captain William O'Shea, who was now suing her for divorce and citing Parnell as the cause.

Parnell's fate might have been averted – by money.

The Victorians were hypocrites, if sometimes for the best reasons. They could tolerate scandals that remained private – Parnell's relationship with Katie (she was never 'Kitty') O'Shea was known in political circles. But William O'Shea broke the rules by making the situation public.

Sordidly, the motive all came down to money. Katie O'Shea had always known she was the likely heir to her aunt's estate. Mrs Maria Wood – known as 'Aunt Ben' – was a wealthy, childless widow. Throughout her life, Aunt Ben had always helped Mrs O'Shea financially, and provided her with an income that gave her some financial independence.

Aunt Ben, who was well-educated but somewhat severe, had conventional, Victorian, Protestant morals; nobody wanted to upset her. Thus, Katie's involvement with Parnell (and gradual estrangement from her husband) had to be kept deadly secret from her aunt. Katie O'Shea lived in constant fear of Aunt Ben discovering the true circumstances of her life: that she lived with Parnell, not O'Shea, despite O'Shea giving all the appearances of being a complaisant husband.

But O'Shea, a gambler with a history of bankruptcy – who was a mixture of 'vanity, calculation and naiviety' – was always short of money. He assumed that on Aunt Ben's death he would receive a large slice of the inheritance, while he remained, legally, Katie's husband. Aunt Ben lived on and on and on, finally dying in 1889, at the grand old age of ninety-eight.

At last, Katharine O'Shea felt free. Her biographer, Elisabeth Kehoe, describes how Katie and Parnell took long walks together 'in the glorious spring of the year', feeling young and happy and in love.

But Captain O'Shea, bitter that he had not been included in Aunt Ben's will (worth over £200,000 then, which would be several millions today), then decided to go public with the divorce and begin proceedings.

If only Katie had paid him off, either earlier, or then. Then the public divorce could have been avoided, and Parnell might have continued to lead the Irish Party, without the subsequent, painful, 'split' that loomed over Irish politics for the following twenty-five years. Money might have meant that the entire history of Irish politics, north and south, would have been different.

The reality of life on the Lake Isle of Innisfree

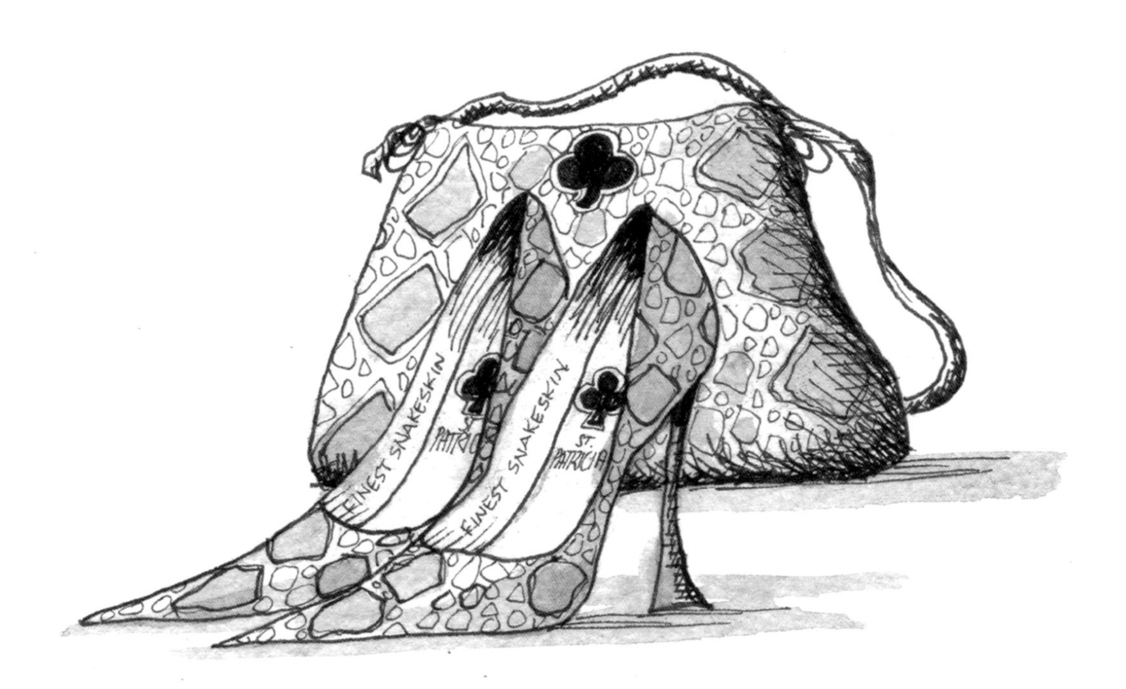
FINEST SNAKESKIN
FINEST SNAKESKIN
ST. PATRICIA

What if Irish historians told the full story about womens' contribution to Irish history?

Myles Dungan

We might start to hear less about the Countess and Granuaile and discover some remarkable women whose achievements have been suppressed by male chauvinist historians for generations. Among these female pioneers are the following neglected figures:

Brenda the Navigator: a sixth-century explorer who led voyages of discovery to the Canaries, the Azores, Tír na nÓg, and an imposing land mass to the west of Ireland that should properly be known today as the United States of Brenda. It is distressing to note the complicity of the esteemed composer Shaun Davey in suppressing acceptance of the historical and cultural significance of this courageous Kerrywoman. He bowed to pressure in 1980 and renamed his otherwise excellent orchestral suite *The Brenda Voyage*.

St Patricia: a fifth-century couturier who designed a highly regarded line of snakeskin shoes and handbags under the 'Shamrock' logo. The business foundered when she ran out of raw material because of the resentful sibling rivalry of her pietistic brother, Patrick.

Danielle O'Connell (also known as the Liberatrix): she fought and won female emancipation only to see, at the last minute, the word 'female' deleted from the enabling act and replaced by the word 'Catholic'.

Even where gender has been acknowledged, as in the case of St Bridget, the real achievement has been understated. Bridget is depicted as a plaster saint. In fact, she was a sixth-century dentofacial innovator. Described in historical literature as a 'retainer', she was, in fact, responsible for the invention of the orthodontic retainer. The proof of this is to be found in an expression previously thought to have referred to the customary preliminaries in Irish sexual foreplay, i.e. 'Brace yourself, Bridget'. The quote actually comes from a cutting remark made by an apoplectic male rival and should in fact read 'Brace YOURSELF, Bridget'.

Paul Revere's midnight ride comes to an unexpected end

THE NATIONAL TRUST
WELCOME TO
LAS VEGAS

Not their cup of tea
David McCullagh

'This is one small step for a man, one giant leap for the British Empire.'
Wait, what?
When Neil Armstrong landed on the moon on 20 July, 1969, he naturally planted the flag of the country that had launched him and his comrades to their date with destiny.
But the United States of America only exists because of almost unbelievable arrogance, stupidity and obstinacy on the part of Great Britain.
At numerous points along the American path to independence, the separatist desire could have been turned aside by compromise and a willingness to see the other chap's point of view.
What if, for instance, London had listened to the unrest over taxation that was demonstrated at the Boston Tea Party?
The colonists objected to taxation without representation, and they had a point. But when they dumped that tea into Boston Harbour in December 1773, it was still possible to imagine a solution that would not lead to the War of Independence.
Instead, the British Parliament decided to take a tough line with the uppity Americans, introducing coercive legislation, which in turn prompted the colonies to come together in the First Continental Congress.
At this point, it began to dawn on some in London that the hard line might not be the wisest one.
For instance, William Pitt the Elder wanted to recognise colonial self-government, but this was rejected by the House of Lords, providing proof, if proof were needed, of that body's instinctive reactionary stupidity.
Eventually London climbed down, promising to lift taxes on colonies that contributed to the defence of the Empire.
But by then, it was too late, and it was on course to lose the bulk of its North American empire, thanks to French help for the colonists.
So, what if Pitt's suggestion had been adopted?
The thirteen colonies, along with Canada, would have remained part of the British Empire. While they may in time have developed a separate identity, complete separation would hardly have been inevitable.
They might have joined the two World Wars on time; they might have learned to spell properly; and the World Series might have been a cricket competition.
And right now, a lot of attention would be paid to who will become the next Prime Minister of British North America – Lady Hillary Clinton, or Sir Donald Trump.

Little is known about the meeting between Granuaile and Queen Elizabeth I

MIWOK
BINGO
FOR
BUCKS

What if Francis Drake had never left San Francisco?

Elgy Gillespie

In 1579, pirate adventurer Francis Drake explored the Americas, pillaging and scaring the locals and Spanish up the Pacific West Coast in an effort to find Asia.

His *Golden Hind* was tiny and listing, its rigging in tatters. It was about to founder. But what hostilities would they meet if they dropped anchor?

The *Golden Hind* had survived skirmishes with furious locals and Spaniards on both coasts around the Horn. But it was now capsizing. So with their boat taking on water, Drake and his men careened at high tide onto a beach on what is now Point Reyes, just north of what is San Francisco Bay. The 'stynkinge fogges' they recorded in their log had prevented them from noticing the Bay or much else.

From out of the fog, Miwok tribesmen approached the starving sailors on the beach. To the sailors' surprise they offered them oysters and clams, and gestured towards a circle of round reed huts and busy villagers not far away.

Soon, instead of fighting, they were sitting around a fire pit over a mighty feast of smoked salmon, bear, venison, acorn bread, buckeye porridge, and baskets of unfamiliar berries and hazelnuts, washed down by a hearty brew of something alcoholic tasting like chocolate, and made from sugared pine nuts.

While the ravenous sailors fell upon the food, Miwoks found saplings and wood to repair spars in the *Hind*. Miwok women prepared beds for guests by plumping brush-filled bolsters and coverlets.

At the climax of the feast, the *hoypu* or chief presented Captain Drake with a feather cloak of eagle and osprey feathers, with poems of admiration, and friendship songs from the *malén*, or female chief.

The favorite Miwok pastime being gambling, they then used clamshells to play the 'Hand Game' and 'Bones'.

This description of the Miwok 'potluck' is from the *Golden Hind*'s log, along with their music and best-loved poem, 'We Are Dancing on the Rim of the World'.

In return, Drake stuck the flag of St George in the ground and claimed California for the Virgin Queen and New Albion.

Thoughts of possibilities soon entered Drake's head as he watched the game-playing of the Miwoks, and decided he did not wish to leave this perfect society.

Instead, he produced his pack of cards and taught the Miwok Two-Hand Monte, Texas Hold'Em, Poker, Baccarat and Bingo for Bucks. Within a month, the Miwok were building casinos on the Pacific coastline, with thatched cabins and community tents for pow-wows and potlucks.

Four oyster and clam bars later, Los Dagos nightclub, a Starbucks, 2,000 slot machines, and a bowling alley followed. The Miwok gambling empire spread across America, and Francis Drake became *hoypu* of all.

What if?

THE BEATLES
LOVE ME DO
REJECT

What if Dick Rowe had signed on the dotted line?

Barry Devlin

The Beatles were an English pop band who released a number of little-known singles between 1962 and their break-up in 1963. The band line-up comprised Pete Best (drums and vocals), George Harrison (lead guitar and vocals), John Lennon (rhythm guitar and vocals), and Paul McCartney (bass guitar and vocals).

The band's brief recording career began in November 1961 when their then manager, Brian Epstein, sent demo tapes to Decca's A&R man, Dick Rowe: Rowe reacted favourably to the band's audition in the studios in West Hampstead. (Though he had said at the time that 'guitar groups are on the way out'.)

Rowe signed the band on 8 January, 1962.

Though Lennon and McCartney had been the group's singers on stage up to this point, Rowe felt strongly that drummer Pete Best was the band's main attraction. Accordingly, Best sang lead vocals on their first single, which was produced by Norrie Paramor – Helen Shapiro's producer – in Decca's studios on 8 February.

Rowe attempted to replace guitarist George Harrison with Mike Maxfield from Manchester band the Coasters before the session, but in the end it was Harrison's guitar that appeared on the single, the A-side of which featured the ballad 'Till There Was You' – with Paramor's signature string stylings – coupled with 'Three Cool Cats' on the B-side...

The single, released on 4 March, reached Number 38 in the UK charts.

Decca felt that a tour supporting Helen Shapiro would help the band's June follow-up, 'Sheik of Araby' – again featuring Pete Best on vocals – which had failed to enter the UK Top 50, but after John Lennon was arrested for grafitti-ing Shapiro's limousine ('don't treat us like a child' was spray-painted in red on the near-side fenders and doors), the band was removed from the tour roster.

Lennon at this point suggested to Norrie Paramor that a more 'beat-style' approach was needed, and the band played Rowe a number of self-penned numbers. (The tape has been lost, but pencilled titles on the box read 'Please, Please Him', 'She Loves You, Yeah', and 'I Want to Hold Her Hand'.) Paramor and Rowe rejected these, but in response to McCartney's and Lennon's appeals to be allowed to sing, their next single – released in time for the Christmas market – was a three-part harmony version of Brenda Lee's 'Rockin' Around the Christmas Tree'. This also failed to chart.

At this point, John Lennon, dispirited by the failure of the group to 'become as big as the Shadows', left and was replaced by comedian Kenny Lynch. Decca released the group from their contract in March 1963, and after a brief spell at Oriole, where they recorded but never released a single called 'Love Me Do', the band split up in September.

Ironically, the other group who auditioned in Decca's studios on that January day in 1962 was none other than Brian Poole and the Tremeloes. Dick Rowe rejected them in favour of the Beatles. Poole and the gang – after signing to Parlophone – famously became the band that defined pop and rock music, right up until today.

And Dick Rowe became famous – or infamous – as the man who turned down the Tremeloes...

10th June 1904: Writer is distracted by shoe bargains

BUS

The Aztec discovery of Ireland
Frank Cottrell-Boyce

The westward expansion of the Aztec Empire during the reign of Moctezuma I reached the Gulf of Mexico in 1458. Having conquered the land from coast to coast, 'the archer of the heavens' declared it his manifest destiny to conquer the sea too. A flotilla of great rafts set sail from Tenaxticpac. The Gulf Stream soon brought these to Inishboffin. As the rafts rode so low in the waves, the islanders got the impression that the Aztecs were walking on the water. This, together with the fact that they were covered in gold, led them to believe that the war party was the Second Coming. They were only too happy to oblige, therefore, when the Aztecs commanded them to build a massive stone pyramid. They were surprised and disappointed when the Aztecs then used this pyramid as a venue for the mass sacrifice of the islands' entire adult male population. However, the huge quantities of chocolate and potatoes that the conquerors brought with them were seen as some kind of compensation. Realising the power of these products, Moctezuma drew up the Statutes of Kildare, which said that anyone who refused to dress in the Aztec style would not be allowed to drink chocolate or eat spuds. Illuminated manuscripts of the period show that very soon even monks and nuns were going round dressed in feathers and gold.

The Aztecs quickly instituted a massive programme of road and pyramid building that was emulated by the rest of Europe. To this day the great temple complex at New Tenochtlican, Co. Cavan is a wonder of the world, and the annual celebrity sacrifice a highlight of the Hiberno-Aztec social calendar. Irish labour is still first choice when it comes to construction work.

Why all archaeological finds must be reported

SPORT
IRELAND
CHAMPIONS
FURIOUS KEANE STORMS OUT OF PRESS CONFERENCE
"THIS IS RIDICULOUS" SAYS KEANE AT DEPARTURES GATE
IRISH INDO
IRELAND WINNERS
RUBBI

Dreams of Roy
Cathal Mac Coille

Fantasy football is the stuff of dreams without limits...

It's July 1, 2002, the day after the World Cup Final. Ireland has beaten Brazil. RTÉ's Tommie Gorman is back in Cheshire, to ask again on a nation's behalf if Ireland's captain is willing to rejoin his teammates.

'Roy, do you remember how a month ago I pleaded with you to rejoin the Irish World Cup squad, and at first you said no?'

'How could I forget? I was called a liar, remember?'

'There was a lot of angry talk from you, and from your manager Mick McCarthy, and some of your teammates. And of course we remember how it ended with you leaving. But the fact is we got through to the second round, and the Taoiseach Bertie Ahern flew you back to Japan in the government jet. The squad put the past behind you, and then you beat Spain.'

'On penalties, Tommie, don't forget that. Nothing to write home about.'

'And then in the semi-final, you beat South Korea.'

'And that was on penalties too, *after* extra time. Normal time should have been enough. Tactics were a farce. Half the government running onto the pitch like eejits, clapping us on the back like we're heroes. We were lucky, that's all.'

'And then the final. A wonderful day, for all of us. Roy, we'd never have won that game without you, even though you were sent off.'

'Ronaldo deserved it. And I won't apologise for breaking his leg.'

'No-one's asking you to apologise, Roy, and Alex Ferguson said it was a fair tackle. But the unforgettable fact is that your team won in the end.'

'But they didn't score, Tommie, or even look like scoring. Same old bloody story. Manager out of his depth, again. More bumpy training pitches, the team down the back of the plane again, the officials in first class, and all the rest of it.'

'But, Roy, we're the world champions.'

'On bloody penalties, Tommie, again. A joke, we are.'

'But we're all proud and happy. Would you not reconsider your decision to stay away from the welcome-home ceremony in Dublin? Think of all the children who dream about you, who look up to you as a role model. They'd love to see you.'

'No way. More backslapping, and politicians saying how great the country is, and people getting drunk and youngsters puking in the street, and people singing "Olé Olé" over and over, and the rest of the world laughing at us.

'We didn't deserve to win. Quarter-final, semi-final, and final ... all won on bloody penalties. Ridiculous.

'I refuse to be part of it, Tommie, and that's that.'

So the row goes on, as the nation consoles itself with World Cup success. Then I wake up.

In 1874, archaeologists excavate a dolmen in Sligo with unexpected results

2ND
1ST
3RD
JEUX
OLYMPIQUES
MCMXXIV

What if the Great War had been over by Christmas?

Frank McNally

Football played a central role in the success of the ceasefires that had spread along the Western Front over Christmas and New Year, 1914. So when formal peace talks began in February, they were accompanied by an informal European championship involving teams from the combatant countries.

The Irish XI, drawn mostly from prisoners of war and managed by Sir Roger Casement (who, for mysterious reasons, happened to be in Germany at the time), were the tournament's surprise package, being one of the last four teams. But the Germans won the title, beating England on penalties, and the resultant goodwill helped seal the peace agreement, signed by all sides in March.

Ireland's Home Rule Act took effect later that year, with the new southern parliament eventually extending its control over 28.5 counties, after Dublin unionist Edward Carson agreed to cede Fermanagh, Tyrone, and South Armagh in exchange for a Hong Kong-sized enclave around Kingstown.

Even so, at the funeral of O'Donovan Rossa in August, Patrick Pearse made his 'the fools, the fools' speech, just as we know it. But with self-government now a reality, the debate about Ireland's future had become dominated by economics.

Amid a general nervousness in the real estate sector, the value of Fenian graves had temporarily slumped (a bit like Scottish oil prices a century later). So, despite continued manoeuvres by the Volunteers and the Citizen Army, 1916 would pass without the Rising.

There were some isolated Republican attacks in later years, especially in Munster. But these were put down ruthlessly by a young policeman named Tom Barry. Deprived of a chance to 'see what war was like', he had never joined the British Army in 1917, instead following his father into the RIC, where he rose rapidly through the ranks to become Chief Constable at twenty-seven.

Others whose lives were dramatically different as a result of the 1914 armistice included Thomas McDonagh, who, as Yeats had foreseen, 'won fame in the end'. His many awards include the 1936 Nobel Prize for Literature. Not that Yeats had ever written the poem with that line. His notebooks of the period suggest he was toying with a phrase about the birth of some 'terrible beauty', but never found a way to use it.

Of course, in the universe where the war ended early, many things happened, just as they would have done had the conflict continued for four years. In 1924, for example, when sports-themed art was a discipline at the Olympic Games in Paris, Jack B. Yeats still won a silver medal for the *Liffey Swim*. The only difference, in this version, is that he was beaten to the gold by a German painter named Adolf Hitler.

Hitler had been one of the last casualties of the short-lived war, suffering a serious head wound just before Christmas 1914. Indirect effects of the injury included his life-long pacifism and a belated breakthrough in his ability to draw the human figure (as opposed to just buildings). He was finally accepted by the Vienna School of Art in 1915, as a mature student. And he won the Olympic Gold for his depiction, based on sketches made at the time, of a football match in No Man's Land.

'There. Finished at last.'

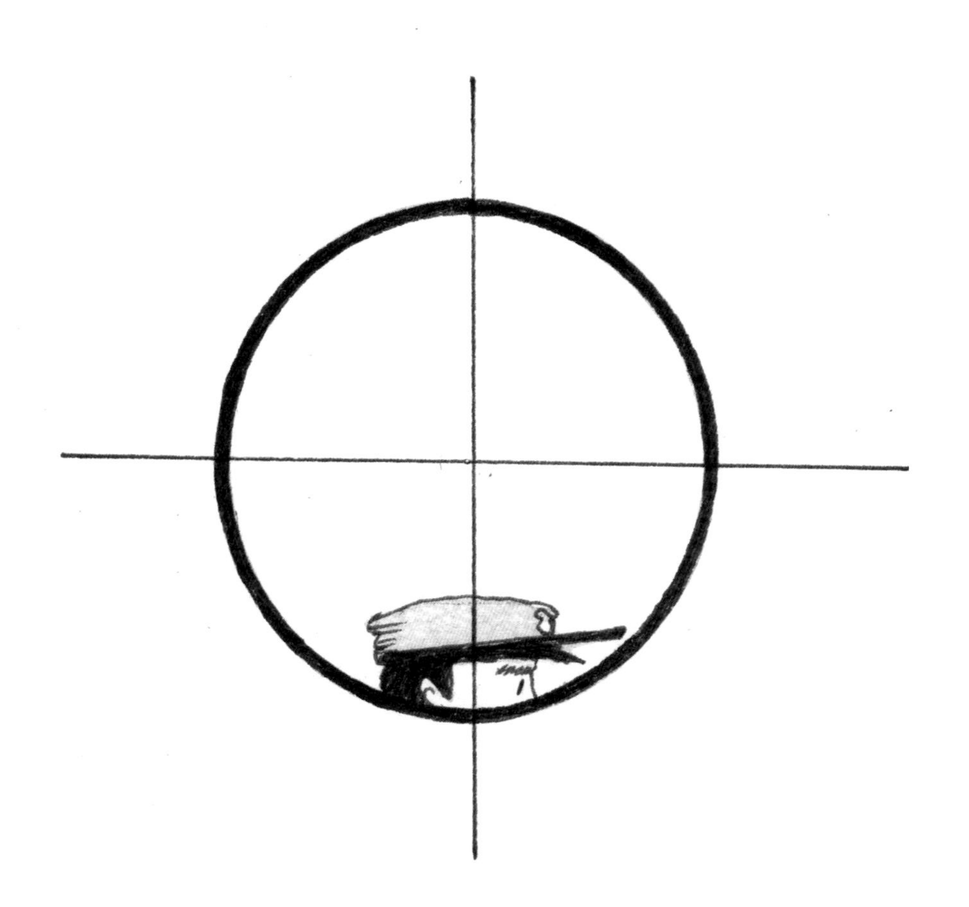

What if 'The Big Fella' had been short?

Colm Tobin

Growing up in Clonakilty, I lived in the shadow of Michael Collins. He wasn't following me around or anything … but he was a totemic figure in our local history, and we were made aware of him from early on, usually when threatened by adults: 'Pick up those toys or the Big Fella will get you.'

There was no questioning Collins's red-blooded, virile allure. Even his nickname exudes a sort of big-brotherly manliness and Celtic power. He was a symbol of that brand of patriarchal, kick-you-up-the-hole, Irish masculinity; a brand that finds its modern representation in a more watered-down form, e.g. Press Office photocalls of Simon Coveney emptying fish-boxes into the arse-end of refrigerated lorries.

It was around 1996 when the wider world began to take notice of Collins. International audiences were introduced to him by Liam Neeson's performance in Neil Jordan's unforgettable movie, *Taken, 1916*. And the rest is contentious, revisionist history.

In *Taken, 1916*, we were not only shown Collins as a revolutionary hero, but also Collins as an oily sex symbol, swanning around Dublin, cracking jokes, driving Kitty O'Shea wild … this wasn't some thicko from West Cork, more a Justin Timberlake for the international independence movement. And, having looked for you, Mick would find you, and he would kill you.

But what if Collins had been a man of smaller stature – say around five-foot-two-and-a-half? Would his rise to prominence in the Republican movement have been thwarted by size-ist prejudice? He might never have gone to London, having failed to pass the height restrictions for the post office. Would he have just been stuck living in West Cork, working in a resort lodge and spa, and combing the beach with bin bags to prepare seaweed baths for Protestants?

Would Dev really have sent this man, no taller than Ronnie Corbett, to ~~sign his own death warrant~~ negotiate a peace treaty with the British Empire? And even if he did, might Lloyd George have just sat on him by mistake? And what then for Anglo-Irish relations? And would all of these vertical challenges have combined to give Collins a dangerously megalomaniacal strain of *short man syndrome*, as with Adolf Hitler, Tom Cruise, and Bono?

And after all the years of civil war, would his notorious assassin, having taken aim and prepared to fire, simply have missed his head by a few inches? What then for the Irish Republic? With Collins alive, he would have had to face the disappointing reality of nation building. And nation building was no fun in a country where priests outnumbered people, women were chained to signposts for days and forced to dance at crossroads, and you could barely leave the house without getting a) TB or b) drowned in a torrent of Bovril.

You'd wonder if Michael Collins would be so lauded as a symbol of rebellion and patriotism today. Would we even have erected that statue in his name? If we had, it'd be significantly shorter.

I suppose we'll never know.

It's amazing the difference a foot makes.

Could have been worse

LEO BURDOCK
POISSON
ET
POMMES FRITES

What if the French had conquered Ireland?

Turtle Bunbury

Bantry Bay, 21 December, 1796. Wolfe Tone was absolutely gutted. 'There cannot be imagined a situation more provokingly tantalising than mine at this moment,' he lamented in his diary. 'Within view, almost within reach of my native land, and uncertain whether I shall ever set foot in it. We were near enough to toss a biscuit ashore.'

Tone had devoted several years to organising this *Expédition d'Irlande*: a major invasion of the southern Irish coast by a fleet of 43 ships and nearly 15,000 French troops.

All had been going reasonably smoothly until the weather changed and the Atlantic Ocean became a hellhole of perpetual tempests. Most of the French ships actually reached the Irish coast, but they were unable to land and, as the first vessel began to crash and sink upon the rocks, the rest turned and fled back home.

But what if the French had landed successfully? What if they had overpowered the British Redcoats who garrisoned the southern shores and then united with the tens of thousands of Irish men and women who were longing to oust the dastardly British from the island?

I've long considered it a shame that Ireland was not conquered by the French, if only for a generation or two.

It would have done wonders for our cuisine. The French have always been champions in the kitchen, and they would have quickly put an end to the Irish dependence on potatoes and introduced other foodstuffs. They'd have certainly come up with new and better ways to cook spuds, as per Madame Mérigot's best-selling 1794 publication, *La Cuisinière Républicaine* (*The Female Republican Cook*), considered the world's first potato cookbook.

Had the French landed at Bantry, perhaps the sunny south would have become a haven of exotic vineyards, ooh la la. That said, when the fateful storms kyboshed the French in 1796, those ill winds proved good news for Ireland's snails and frogs, as they have remained successfully uneaten for over two centuries since.

Our architectural heritage would surely have benefitted from a Gallic makeover – boulevards in our market towns, a dash of *trompe l'oeil* on our bungalows, a hint of the avant-garde on our housing estates, complete with shutters on the outside.

The Napoleonic Code guaranteed freedom of religion, although one suspects that the good Protestants of Ulster would have defiantly declared '*Non*'.

The inheritance laws outlined by the code insisted that all land be shared equally between all sons. In Ireland, that would have meant that every Irishman would have owned about seven square inches of land by 1896, and we'd have become a nation of worm farmers.

As the nineteenth century wore on, there would have been mounting resentment of a French-controlled Ireland as young Irishmen were compulsorily drafted to serve in the French Army. By 1896 the Irish may well have found themselves asking Britain to help crack the shackles of French imperialism.

The Napoleonic Code also took the brazen step of specifying that government jobs should only be given to people with the right qualifications but perhaps, even today, that would be pushing things a step too far.

Dormez bien, mes amis.

If Maud Gonne had said 'Yes'

1916
HEROIC
DEEDS
IRELAND'S GREAT DEAD
MARTYRDOM FOR BEGINNERS
DYING FOR IRELAND
101 GREAT DEAD PEOPLE
DEATH HINTS TIPS

If De Valera had had the decency to get himself executed in 1916

Declan Lynch

If Eamon de Valera had been executed in 1916, we would now regard him as another of our revered martyrs: a beautiful loser, a crazy dreamer who could have been anything; that he turned out to be one of history's great monsters is of course unfortunate, not just in itself, but because it makes you wonder how some of the other men of 1916 might have turned out.

If Dev had perished, and Pearse had survived, the fact that Pearse would in all likelihood have also handed us over to the Catholic Church for their sport would have created a great if entirely mistaken yearning in us for the lost Long Fellow – we would imagine that had he lived, he, with his famously mathematical brain, might have been immune to the irrationalities of all religion, constructing instead some sort of Scandinavian ideal which would be more in keeping with his cerebral tastes.

What fools we would have been.

Michael Collins would probably have lived a little longer if Dev had checked out in 1916, though as a general rule the record shows that the longer our heroes live, the less heroic they tend to become.

De Valera himself never revealed his inner thoughts on this – or indeed on any other issue – yet there must have been moments when he felt that surviving 1916, while it undoubtedly conferred certain short-term benefits, was, on the whole, one of the most catastrophic career moves in all of Irish history.

We cannot even fathom the concept of De Valera as a much-loved leader of the doomed revolution, or as a much-loved anything, due to this utterly misguided insistence of his to go on living.

Would there have been the Civil War without him? Frankly, there were probably enough deeply damaged individuals knocking around back then to ensure that for Paddy, nothing would ever run smoothly. But let's pin that on him anyway, for not having the basic decency to get himself in front of a British firing squad, and enough of the bullshit.

How easy his soul would have rested without the foundation of Fianna Fail on his conscience, or the drafting of the 1937 Constitution with his great mate Archbishop McQuaid.

What a different Dev it would have been – a far, far better Dev.

One who, as he awaited the executioner, could reasonably have foreseen himself in the fullness of time being played by, say, Aidan Quinn, with a bit of an American accent, even a little charm, rather than Alan Rickman warming up for later roles as the Sheriff of Nottingham and Rasputin.

Instead, because De Valera did not get what was coming to him, all we got was another fifty years of the truth.

And that's never much good for Paddy.

The curse of writer's block

NOTICE
HURLING
IS NOW
FORBIDDEN
for health
&
safety reasons

Setanta's sport

Feargal Murphy

Setanta was competing with his friend Ferdia for left half-back position in the county hurling team. He was also eager to join the Red Line Knights, the army of his uncle, King Conor MacGregor, but this was impossible as they were on strike at the time.

His uncle Conor was going to meet with Culann, the manager of the county team, to have a session and discuss the team selection process. Setanta's uncle wanted him to accompany him so that he could demonstrate his superb hurling skills, but Setanta stayed back for a club game, saying he would catch up later.

He set out after his uncle later that day, still in his club kit, arriving at Culann's when the session was well under way. Culann had a mean hound trained in mixed canine arts. As Setanta approached, the dog started barking and eyed Setanta angrily. Keen to show off his prowess, Setanta threw his sliotar in the air and pucked it straight at the dog. The dog caught the sliotar in his mouth as Culann and Conor came out to see what was causing the commotion. The dog shook his head and bit into the sliotar, crushing it to pieces. Bits of the sliotar flew in all directions. A sliver of sliotar found its way into Culann's ear, causing deafness in that ear, this being the origin of the famous slogan, 'Ulster says "what"?'

The now furious dog pounced on Setanta and snapped at his hands to get him to release his hurley, turning his hands red with blood.

Seeing Setanta's plight, Conor immediately banned hurling throughout the island due to its violent nature, indirectly leading to Kilkenny's dominance in football. Setanta was sent to the doghouse and invented the satellite transmission of sports events. Very little is known of Setanta after this event.

Setanta's friend Ferdia rose to prominence in athletics and his name was used by the Ford motor company for the short-lived Ford Ferdia, which was built in Ardee.

Ferdia's athletic career faded after a doping/magic spells scandal, and he took up with a bad crowd and fell under the influence of a powerful woman in the west.

He was finally arrested and convicted for cattle smuggling.

But for a few seconds, Jonah and the Whale might have been a shorter story

IRISH TIMES PROPERTY
GRACIOUS LIVING IN THE VALE OF TEARS
VIEWING ESSENTIAL

Adamant Eve

Jim Lockhart

What if that Adam and Eve story was just misheard, and it was actually about Adamant Eve, so-called because, like, no way would she touch that crappy-looking apple?

See, the Serpent had been quite pleased with his sales spiel, but Eve wasn't having any of it. Her eyes narrowed. 'What in the hell is that?' she asked. 'How do I know what it's after gettin' sprayed with? And lookit, every leaf here is crawling with disgustin' slugs and greenflies. This so-called garden needs a good makeover. Them shrubs don't go with yer Good-and-Evil tree. What you need is a nice little arch here, and a trellis over there with roses or something, and you'll need a skip to clear all this rubbish. I want that buddleia gone; it makes the place look like a right kip. And hydrangeas make me vomit. *Vomit*. What are them things – Cedars of Lebanon? Well I'm sick of them!'

The Serpent heaved a weary sigh and slid off back to God, who'd been rapping testily on the arm of his throne, not a happy man.

'Jesus, what are we going to do with this ratbag?' said the Serpent.

'Leave the family out of this,' God said. 'You have zero clue about selling to women. I'd have presented the apple in a nice pink box, nestled in fruit-fragrant tissue paper with a dinky little ribbon and a Butler's chocolate.'

'But it was naturally beautiful,' wheedled the Serpent. 'It was organic, for God's sake.'

'I said leave me out of it,' God snapped. 'You had one job. One. Job. Did you not show her the glossy brochure for the Vale of Tears?'

'She wasn't buying it. She's adamant. Adamant Eve. Oh, why can't a woman be more like a man?'

'Shut up with the musicals already,' God said. 'Put on Bette Midler one more time, and I swear I will literally scream'.

'Oh, puh-leeeze!' said the Serpent. 'See, that's more of it now. You're always undermining me, always. Chip, chip, chip. No wonder my self-esteem is in shreds.'

God said, 'Pull yourself together and stop queening. I need this place cleared. The planning permission is in the bag. Do you know how many luxury apartments with south-facing balconies we can put in here? And a boutique hotel, and a spa. And a golf course.'

'Golf!' snorted the Serpent.

'You wouldn't understand,' God sighed. 'Out on the golf course, I feel free. All cares fall away'.

The Serpent looked down, or rather across. 'Where did you get those vile diamond socks?' he said.

'Golf is Heaven,' God murmured absently. 'Listen,' the Serpent perked up. 'I may have a solution. Why don't we wait until she's asleep and steal one of her ribs and make another creature from it that would be more . . . I dunno, gullible or biddable or . . .'

There was an icy pause from God. 'Oh, *great,*' he said. 'Now you've really lost it. Wonderful. Wonderful. Not remotely daft. Not bonkers in the least. Steal a rib, eh? Oh, yes. They'd be writing about that for thousands of years, and no mistake!'

Robin Hood is arrested, tried and executed

ANTI WRINKLE CREAM
DEATH B GONE
IT REALLY WORKS
Eternal Youth moisturiser
LYRICAL O' WAX

Skin deep

Tara Flynn

The worst thing that happened to Tír na nÓg was Oisín talking to the press about it. If he hadn't used his last seaside gasps to tell all, Tír na nÓg would still be the idyll he remembered. He's dead now, of course.

Who knew winning Spa of the Year would be a poisoned chalice? Now you can review the place on SpaAdvisors.

'I never want to leave. Can't recommend highly enough,' types Margaret from Howth. You'd never guess her age, now, just by looking. Only by her stories would you know it. (They say she had a fling with Bowie. I say 'they'. I mean 'she'.)

Getting there is as difficult as you've heard. You have to stumble on the beach by chance, just at the moment the white horse sets his hooves upon the sand. It's hard to plan around it. But if the SpaAdvisor reviews are anything to go by, it's worth the wait.

'I never dreamed my skin would glow like this again!' Doris, ninety, Leitrim.

'My husband of fifty years fancies me! I haven't seen him in ten, but he loves the selfies I send. It's a miracle.' Breda, seventy-two, Athlone.

No one speaks about the secret treatments – why would they share that? – but of Niamh, who conducts them all, they wax lyrical. In fact, lyrical waxing is rumoured to be an incredible treatment. It is said to be entirely pain-free.

They say Niamh is blonde, her hair swinging loose to her waist when she shakes it free from its grip at the end of the day. Despite the island's westerly location, she has no wisps or frizzes or split ends. She is tall, but manages to look everyone in the eye; then they feel tall too. She wears no make up but is as radiant as the dawn – for which you're encouraged to rise, daily, and salute the sun, which seems to perma-shine. She's never seen to eat, but sips regularly from a bottle that seems to be filled with a fine mist. She does no interviews and has no Instagram account. And no one leaves her side til they are ready to leave and never return. Then, only then, at the end, can the experience be reviewed.

Like Oisín discovered, along with the journalist who documented his demise, even the most magical treatment can only push out the end – it can't eliminate it. And the price? Life on an isolated island where no one smiles for fear of wrinkles.

They say everyone would go there if they could. They say we all would love to turn back time and not feel pain. If we could be twenty forever. If hot stones could heal sore muscles and torn hearts. If you could be clear-skinned and lithe and shiny and never look back.

Now Tír na nÓg is overrun with the smooth and shallow. Their eyes, though. Look into their eyes.

God wakes up and realises the whole thing was just a really bad dream

1931
CHARLES CHAPLIN
BEST ACTOR
LITTLE HITLER

How *Little Hitler* caused the Second World War

Robert Cullen

2016 saw Adolf Hitler's magnum opus, *Mein Kampf*, finally released from copyright restrictions, and already Hollywood has two films in the works.

One is reported to star Irish actor Colin Farrell as the German warmonger, the other more controversial movie will star Woody Allen in what is expected to be his last role before serving his prison sentence.

The two-volume autobiography of Hitler was always a source of controversy and, through the devastation of the Second World War, a very real source of conflict.

It was, of course, Metro Goldwyn Mayer's 1931 adaptation, *Little Hitler*, starring silent movie star Charlie Chaplin, that caused the German Chancellor to declare war on the United States (home of MGM) and Great Britain (birthplace of Chaplin).

Hitler wrote his autobiography at the relatively young age of thirty-four while in prison for a failed coup in Munich. He didn't write the story himself, but dictated it to his co-conspirator Rudolf Hess (who would be played in the film by Greta Garbo).

The content of *Mein Kampf* was seen as controversial and inciteful at the time, and when a copy was sent to Marcus Loew, the Jewish head of MGM, he saw the potential to remove some of the more inflammatory anti-Semitic aspects of it and turn it into a slapstick comedy vehicle for Chaplin.

The film was released in the spring of 1931 to huge critical acclaim in the United States. However, when a copy was reluctantly sent by Loew to Hitler, the German demanded that the film be scrapped and not see the light of day.

In the end, *Little Hitler* would earn MGM over $5 million at the box office. For its star, Chaplin, there would be an Academy Award and an OBE from King George V.

Hitler, enraged at his portrayal as a short, angry little man, decided to invade any European country that chose to show the film, starting with Poland and finishing with his failed attempt to invade Russia.

A crowd gathers to watch as Galileo demonstrates his Falling Objects Theory

DIET
COKE

What if Elvis had lived?
Sheila O'Malley

When the Betty Ford Clinic opened in 1982, Elvis was one of its first clients. With a lot of help, he kicked the drug addiction. His 1984 album (the first album released post-treatment) was nominated for a Grammy and featured duets with various famous women, including Dolly Parton, Barbra Streisand, Diana Ross and Linda Ronstadt.

In 1986 he went on a gigantic world tour, breaking audience attendance records everywhere, including the former Yugoslavia.

His 1990 *MTV Unplugged* was as legendary as his 1968 comeback special, the high point being Elvis singing the entirety of 'Amazing Grace' in four different languages. (The single went platinum in three days.)

Quentin Tarantino wrote a role for Elvis in one of his movies. His character had no lines and he only appeared for fifteen minutes; nevertheless, he won a Best Supporting Oscar.

He got married three more times (one being a short-lived remarriage to his first wife, Priscilla). His final marriage, to a woman thirty years his junior, lasted until he died.

In 2003 Elvis launched a program on satellite radio called *Graceland Gearheads*, devoted to all things cars, broadcast out of the Jungle Room at Graceland. It developed an enormous audience, in part because Elvis would give away vehicles at random to lucky callers. Fanatics would call in from all over the country and scream at Elvis about his opinions on cars: 'I'm SICK of you Cadillac people, you all make me SICK. The Ford Mustang is the best car in the world. I've had it, Elvis, I've HAD IT.'

Elvis opened a karate studio in Memphis and hoped it would go international. Instead, it went bankrupt. He opened a restaurant in Memphis. It closed after six months. He bought a dude ranch. It hemorrhaged money before eventually shutting down.

His last album, released when he was eighty-one years old, was a country music album featuring guest artists Miley Cyrus, Adele, Eric Church, Norah Jones and his daughter, Lisa Marie.

In 2005, Elvis, a lifelong amusement-park devotee, had a roller coaster built in the field behind Graceland. Until the end of his life (he died at eighty-three), at 3 a.m. on most quiet Memphis nights, neighbours could hear a loud, rattling, whizzing roar filling the air.

It was Elvis, enjoying a solo ride.

Disgusted, Joe leaves the bog, never to return

The Cattle Raid of Cooley

Lorna Siggins

Pillow talk is a risky business, especially for royalty. And not just any royalty, but Iron Age royalty at that.

There she is, Medb, queen of all of Connacht, lying beside her consort, Ailill, in Roscommon's royal *cruachán* when he whispers 'Finnbennach' in her ear.

This is the name of his beautiful white bull, said to have been once a calf in her herd that 'refused to be owned by a woman'. Ailill taunts her, telling her she has no match.

If there is no greater wrath to witness than a woman scorned, that phrase can only have been coined by someone ignorant of the Táin Bó Cuailgne. Up Medb jumps, summons her troops, and charges them with finding a better animal. A force of 54,000 warriors crosses the mighty River Shannon, then far wider than today, and heads north-east for the Cooley peninsula.

A messenger is despatched to talk to an old man, the owner of a herd of brown cattle and a most fearsome bull.

'If you don't lend it to her for a year, she will have it anyway,' the messenger counsels.

'*Ní maith liom é*,' or, 'buzz off,' the old man replies.

Incandescent at such impudence, Medb sends her warriors to steal the Brown Bull of Cooley in the dead of night. Sadly, she has not consulted her lunar calendar; it is a waning moon, and these soldiers are mountainy men who have only ever gripped the wool of sheep.

As dawn breaks, bearing a red sky with a shepherd's warning, the exhausted warriors return. The bull is indeed a handsome animal, chocolate brown with large pools of eyes and a soft demeanour. By mid-morning, its gentle lowing has turned into an impatient bellow. And so Medb gasps as she looks a little closer.

Heads roll as a furious queen seeks to ensure that her partner will not hear of the animal's gender. However, the nimble messenger is already across the fields, running all the way back to Connnacht to tell Ailill. Storytellers who have thrived on the associated epic battle between Cúchulainn and his foster brother, Ferdia, have to find another Game of Thrones-type plot with equal blood and gore.

And thus begins the infamous tale of Queen Medb and the Brown Cow of Cooley.

What really happened at Dún Aonghasa

DELIVERY SUITE
IT'S A
WELL DONE
TOP LABOUR

If men had babies

Dearbhail McDonald

If men had babies, the human race would face the threat of immediate extinction as men, yet to discover a cure for man flu, enter into a noble and fearless battle with natural childbirth. Confronting Mother Nature with no gas, no air, and no epidural, many of our pioneering heroes do not survive the first set of contractions. Others survive to tell the tale.

In somber tones, the survivors tell of the unthinkable pain, of days spent in labour, groaning in agony in the company of other warriors, of the inhumanity of labouring in corridors and store cupboards because there are not enough delivery suites to accommodate Men-In-Pain.

The crisis escalates as heroic tales, legends really, emerge of the delivery battlefield.

Tales emerge of blood and gore, facing one's enemas, perineal tears, and the gallant, crowning submission to that Ultimate Foe, the Postpartum Stitch.

As the world's population falls into rapid decline, world leaders hold a Global Manliness Summit with women rightly excluded – how could *they* ever understand man's plight?

A Nobel Prize is announced for men who push the boundaries of human endurance and modern science by pushing babies the size of watermelons out of their unshrinking watering holes.

Scientists race against time to find a cure for labour pain and state-of-the-art alternatives to childbirth.

At a special meeting of the 'U-Men' in Geneva, labour pains are declared a gross human rights violation, and sanctions are issued against any country that allows men to give birth as nature intended.

The World Bank and the IMF intervene with emergency fiscal measures as countries battle to subdue mass public-order protests against incredulous, outrageous taxes on 'luxury goods' such as breastfeeding and sanitary pads.

Historians will later describe this revolutionary period as the Menstrual Spring, which gives birth to the Period Power era.

To support the world's population and the brave men populating it, affordable and flexible childcare is written into constitutions.

Infertility treatment is a universal right; the world welcomes the four-day working week, and strict employment laws mean that no man's career shall ever suffer as a result of his Having Babies.

Baby brain is an entirely valid legal defence capable of defeating any criminal or civil charge, and pre-menstrual tension is regarded as the ultimate sexual turn-on.

Because they are men, they naturally enjoy absolute choice and autonomy on the questions of if, when, and how they have babies.

Termination of pregnancy is safe, legal and tax-deductible.

To have babies, men must have periods, prompting a global 'Womb-Men's' rights movement to protect the rights of menstruating men.

Menstruation (it even has the word 'men' in it) is the ultimate expression of manhood, where period stains are celebrated under the cardinal principle that only real men bleed.

Young boys dream of the day they can shout 'I'm on!' as men who reach menopause – this feat is marked by Presidential Decree – are revered for their valour, wisdom and selfless contribution to the human race.

If only men had babies.

Sarajevo, June 1914: Úr Schiller, late for work again

RMS TITANIC
EQUIPMENT LOCKER
SPARE KEY

They're all dead, Dave

John Moynes

On 8 April, 1912, Second Officer David Blair received an order that was to change the course of history, and kill 1,500 people. Blair's order was to disembark and make room for a more experienced officer. This was to be the maiden transatlantic voyage of the *Titanic*, and the White Star Line were not taking any chances with what was, at the time, the largest and most hubristic maritime folly ever constructed.

Blair returned to shore, absentmindedly taking with him a key. It is well known that the designers of the *Titanic* took lifeboats as seriously as MacDonald's take salad, and that attitude extended to all aspects of the ship. Blair's key was the only key that could open the box that contained the only pair of binoculars for the crew of the crow's nest. And a crow's nest without binoculars is merely a device for freezing sailors.

And so, shivering and squinting through a dark night, the lookout men missed the iceberg. The iceberg did not miss them.

A subsequent inquiry held by the United States Congress concluded that the missing key was at fault. Binoculars would have saved the lives of all on board. This was the first time that an inquiry was to blame Blair for needless deaths, but neglected to recommend that Blair be arrested. The inquiry also marked the end of human freedom.

Henceforth, all ships would have to carry enough lifeboats to rescue all passengers and crew. Victims of a sinking in the North Atlantic would now be granted the mercy of a slow death from starvation rather than a quick one in the water. There would be duplicate keys for duplicate boxes containing back-up binoculars. Health and Safety slouched towards Bethlehem to be born.

The tyranny spread from the waves to the shores. Hard hats appeared, Hi Vis jackets, safety harnesses, careful regulations, regiments of kill-joys warned us that this package may contain traces of nuts.

And, tragically, lives were saved. Millions of them, and every one the sort of idiot who needs to be told that sticking one's finger in a plug socket is not a good idea. That bleach is not a refreshing aperitif. That salted peanuts may contain traces of nuts.

There are seven billion people on this planet. If David Blair had done his job properly there would currently be far fewer. But they would, on average, be far better people.

A fine time to lose your theatre tickets

LET'S
TALK
ABOUT
JESUS

The Father, the Son and the Whiskey Spirit – when Robert Johnson found Jesus

Liz Buckley

Robert Leroy Johnson was beat tired. He'd been wandering the dirt tracks of the Mississippi Delta in the fiery midday sun for what seemed like an eternity. The cheap, caseless, wooden guitar strapped behind him had long gone out of tune from the sweat pouring down his back, and he could feel it starting to warp against his beaded skin. A different woman, child and surname in every town for miles claimed him as family, so it was simpler for him to be in no-man's land, keeping his own counsel and keeping his Goddamn balls safe. His journey's aim was never planned further than to take stock at each stumbled-upon crossroads, swigging whiskey to keep his voice from cracking, free to choose his own destiny and generally minding his own damn business.

When he'd left Martinsville a few days back, Robert was a mediocre musician, playing folk songs on street corners and in juke joints for loose change. But Robert Leroy Johnson arrived in Robinsonville possessed of an ability to pick up tunes on first hearing, with a hold over any audience that bordered on the religious. What had happened to him at that quiet crossroads where he'd spent the night practising on his six-string and singing straight up into the starless sky?

He could barely fathom it. A figure had appeared in the dead of night, its face hidden, its voice forbidding. 'Have you heard of Doctor Faust?' it sneered, leaning in so close he could feel only darkness from its shadow. Robert held on to his spectacles, testicles, wallet and watch . . . Doctor Faust? He'd heard of Son House. 'Does this Doctor Faust guy do the lounge circuit? I might have heard his early stuff.'

Then, Lo! A second imposing figure sharply hauled the first away from Robert by its black hair. 'I've got this one, buddy,' he said. 'The Deep South is mine during the summer; we shook on it. Christ. Never trust a time-share.' Robert's saviour stood brightly over him in the moonlight, offering a hand to raise him up. 'Hallelujah!' chimed Robert, strongly feeling his salvation from the previous encounter as well as a distinct improvement in breath.

Who was this second man, this saving grace? Robert Leroy Johnson went into the desert with his new Father/Son/Ghost, and they burnt a bush to keep warm, had some wine and bread, and told stories about a prostitute called Mary Magdelene. It was a great night, and Robert couldn't wait to tell everyone about his new friend. That guy was a straight-up dude. He wanted to sing it from the hilltops. He hadn't just found Jesus, Jesus had found him.

Robert and Jesus were inseparable during Robert's long life, and they formed a band of twelve happy musicians who travelled by the Greyhound bus around the States, preaching songs of kindness and forgiveness. Robert Leroy Johnson eventually died an old man, having just come offstage at the Newport Folk Festival after taking an already opened bottle of beer from his dear friend, Bob 'Judas' Dylan.

What if he's right?

Contributor Biographies

Liz Buckley has worked in music in some form or another since she was a DM-clad, band-T-shirt-wearing teenager. Having grown up working on both sides of the record shop counter, she's made her way through the ranks of the music industry, retail, publishing, licensing, contracts and royalties to be a manager at independent UK label Ace Records, where she now compiles and handles releases. She has her own monthly music column for the all-female staffed *Standard Issue Magazine* and is a new regular contributor on pop for *Digital Spy*. She somehow finds time to write comedy (TV credits include Dave Gorman and Shappi Khorsandi) and has a massively popular cat called Meep, who everyone always asks about before her.

Turtle Bunbury is a best-selling author, award-winning historian and public speaker. His books include *1847 – A Chronicle of Genius, Generosity and Savagery*, *Easter Dawn – The 1916 Rising*, *The Glorious Madness – Tales of the Irish & the Great War* and the award-winning *Vanishing Ireland* series. Turtle is a frequent contributor to television, radio, print and online media including *National Geographic Traveller*, *The World of Interiors* and *Playboy*. www.turtlebunbury.com

Dr Dean Burnett is a doctor of neuroscience, psychiatry lecturer, on-and-off comedian and science writer. He is the author of the popular *Guardian* science blog 'Brain Flapping', and his debut book *The Idiot Brain*. He is Welsh and lives in Cardiff. He doesn't consider either of these things achievements so always mentions them last in biographies.

Charlie Connelly has never scored the winning goal for Charlton Athletic in an FA Cup Final. Despite the stifling and crippling ennui that has settled upon him as a result, he has managed to become the author of fifteen books, including the best-selling *Attention All Shipping: A Journey Round the Shipping Forecast* and *Our Man In Hibernia: Ireland, The Irish and Me*. Charlie has also written comedy scripts for RTÉ and the BBC, and has made a number of documentaries for BBC Radio 4. His television career is notable for the BBC1 *Holiday* programme being canned after thirty-seven years, shortly after he became a presenter.

Frank Cottrell-Boyce is a children's novelist and screenwriter. He won The Guardian Children's Fiction Prize for his book *The Unforgotten Coat* and the Carnegie Medal for *Millions*, which was made into a film by Danny Boyle, with whom he also worked on the opening ceremony of the 2012 Olympic Games. His latest book is *Sputnik's Guide to Life on Earth*.

Robert Cullen has never wandered far from his native Sligo, having trampled the travel bug before it could bite. Working for a newspaper for almost two decades has instilled in him nothing more useful than the ability to spell. His beard hides a multitude of chins.

Barry Devlin is a founder member, writer and vocalist with seminal Irish band Horslips, who are touring again to crowded houses. His film with Liam Neeson, *The Virgin of Las Vegas*, is due to shoot November 2016. His BBC series *My Mother and Other Strangers* has just finished shooting for transmission in the Sunday evening slot on BBC1 this autumn. Everything he does is just as terrifically terrific as he is charmingly charming. He has admired Annie West ever since she asked him to write this stuff.

Myles Dungan, presenter of the *History Show* on RTÉ Radio 1, and a generally overqualified cove, is an older, properly house-trained version of his nephew Philip Boucher Hayes.

Tara Flynn works as a writer, actor and comedian in theatre, radio and TV in Ireland and the UK. Her satirical video *Racist B&B* saw her named Satirist of the Year at the Swift Satire Festival 2013, and she performs regularly with *Dublin Comedy Improv*. TV includes *Irish Pictorial Weekly, Moone Boy, Stewart Lee's Comedy Vehicle* and *Line of Duty*. She has written two satirical books: *You're Grand: the Irishwoman's Secret Guide to Life* and *Giving Out Yards: the Art of Complaint, Irish Style* (Hachette Books Ireland). She is a regular contributor to radio & TV discussion panels and, as you read this, is probably very cross about something.

Tom Foley was the United States Ambassador to Ireland from 2006–2009. He spent most of his career in business acquiring companies in textiles, industrial products, and aviation services. Mr Foley entered public service in 2003 when he was asked by the White House to serve in Iraq as the Director of Private Sector Development. He was awarded the Department of Defense Medal for Distinguished Public Service for his time in Iraq. Mr Foley ran for Governor of Connecticut in 2010 and 2014 and lost by narrow margins in both races. Mr Foley is married to Leslie Fahrenkopf Foley, an attorney, and they live in Greenwich, Connecticut with their five-year-old twins Grace and Reed.

Elgy Gillespie lives in San Francisco where she teaches immigrants English and life skills, and shares an old farmhouse on a hilltop with lodgers, dogs and cats. London-born to an Irish writer and mostly English mother, family connections took her to Trinity and to Dublin. She also still writes for the newspaper where she worked until the late eighties, *The Irish Times*, and she travels whenever she can – most often back to Europe, and including Dublin, of course.

Dr David Robert Grimes is an Irish physicist and cancer researcher, currently based at the University of Oxford. He is also a science writer and frequently contributes to the *Guardian*, *The Irish Times* and the BBC on a wide spectrum of scientific, societal and philosophical topics. He was joint recipient of the 2014 Nature/ Sense About Science Maddox Prize for Standing Up for Science, and can be found on Twitter @drg1985. He is acutely aware that third-person narration makes one sound like Duffman from *The Simpsons*, but persists in doing it anyway.

Mary Kenny is a veteran journalist and writer with a passionate interest in history. She wrote *Goodbye to Catholic Ireland*, *Crown and Shamrock: Love and Hate between Ireland and the British Monarchy* and a biography, *Germany Calling*, of the last man to be hanged in Britain as a traitor, the American-Irish William Joyce (known as Lord Haw-Haw). She lives between Kent and Dublin. She also wrote a play, *Allegiance*, about Winston Churchill's relationship with Michael Collins. www.mary-kenny.com

Jim Lockhart, having learnt little as a penurious student of economics in UCD *metaphor alert*, ran away with the circus and spent further penurious years playing the tin whistle and indulging in bad behaviour* with Horslips, playing in a band being, he reasoned, the perfect excuse for underachieving. Weary ultimately of penury and seeking a buyer for his soul, he latched on to a hapless public broadcasting organisation, which he milked ruthlessly for many years, claiming to be a 'radio producer'. Upon being rumbled, he adopted a 'broadcaster' schtick, which he brazenly continues to maintain, with occasional forays into the old tin whistle carry-on and pretences at 'composing' 'music'. He appears to be married with three adult children, who have not to date disowned him. Rehabilitation attempts are ongoing.
*tautology not intended

Declan Lynch began his writing career at the age of seventeen with *Hot Press* magazine. He now writes for the *Sunday Independent* and is the author of several books, including the acclaimed novels *The Rooms* and *The Ponzi Man*.

Cathal Mac Coille has presented RTÉ's *Morning Ireland* since 2001. His other work includes periods with RTÉ's Belfast staff and the *Sunday Tribune*. Educated at Coláiste Mhuire and UCD, his awards include PPI News Broadcaster of the Year and Oireachtas na Gaeilge Journalist of the Year. Most relevantly, especially for this publication, he has seen Roy Keane playing football and suggesting to others how they should play it properly.

David McCullagh is a journalist and (amateur) historian. He is still, as a teacher once said, not nearly as smart or as funny as he thinks he is.

Dearbhail McDonald is Group Business Editor of Independent News and Media (INM). She is an Eisenhower Fellow (efworld.org) and serves on the board of Fighting Words, the national creative writing centre, is a member of the External Advisory Board of Maynooth University Department of Law, and also serves on the board of the Happy Days Enniskillen International Beckett Festival.

Frank McNally was born in Monaghan. A former national media award winner for his Dáil sketches in *The Irish Times*, he is now chief writer of the paper's daily column, 'An Irishman's Diary'. He lives in Dublin with his wife and three children.

John Moynes is a poet and comedian who lives in early twenty-first-century Dublin. He writes for *Irish Pictorial Weekly* and *Callan's Kicks* and accepts responsibility for 'A Limerick A Day' on broadsheet.ie.

Feargal Murphy is a lecturer in Linguistics in UCD. Ironically, the words that can adequately describe his qualities have not yet been developed, but he is hopeful that some recent development in Indo-European studies will pave the way for the creation of the appropriate lexical items. In the meantime, he remains ineffable.

Sheila O'Malley is a regular film critic for rogerebert.com, and her work has also appeared in *The Dissolve*, *Masters of Cinema*, *Movie Mezzanine*, *Flavorwire*, *Capital New York*, *Fandor*, *Press Play*, and *Bright Wall/Dark Room*. She has contributed video and print essays for *The Criterion Collection*. O'Malley wrote the narration (read by Angelina Jolie) for the tribute reel to legendary actress Gena Rowlands, played at the 2016 Governors Awards, for Rowlands' Lifetime Achievement Oscar. O'Malley writes about actors, movies, and Elvis Presley at her personal site, The Sheila Variations. A short film she wrote, *July and Half of August*, premiered at the 2016 Albuquerque Film and Music Experience.

Lorna Siggins is an *Irish Times* journalist and author.

Colm Tobin is a comedy writer and TV producer with over 50,000 followers on Twitter. As well as writing for *Irish Pictorial Weekly* on RTÉ, he created and co-wrote the children's science shows *Science Fiction* for RTÉ JNR and CBBC, as well as three seasons of *Brain Freeze* for CBBC. *Science Fiction* and *Brain Freeze* have subsequently been sold by Aardman Films in territories all over the word, including Norway, Finland, France, Israel and Australia, and have been featured on Discovery Asia and Al Jazeera. Colm also co-created and co-wrote the satirical RTÉ TV series *Langerland*, and writes regular columns for *The Times* Irish Edition. Originally from Clonakilty, West Cork, Colm now lives in Dublin.

Annie West is an illustrator and cartoonist. Reared on Ronald Searlė, Saul Steinberg and Spike Milligan, Annie graduated from Dun Laoghaire School of Art (IADT) with a degree in TV Production Design. There followed a decade working in the art department on movies, TV and music videos, but all the time thinking about being an illustrator. Annie took a short break in Sligo in 1992 and hasn't been seen since.

Warmest thanks to

Barry Devlin
Cathal MacCoille
Colm Tobin
David McCullagh
Dr David Robert Grimes
Dearbhail McDonald
Declan Lynch
Dr Dean Burnett
Elgy Gillespie
Feargal Murphy
Frank Cottrell-Boyce
Frank McNally
Jim Lockhart
Liz Buckley
Lorna Siggins
Mary Kenny
Miriam Lord
Myles Dungan
Olaf Tyaransen
Patrick Freyne
Robert Cullen
Sheila O'Malley
Tara Flynn
Tom Foley
Turtle Bunbury

Special thanks also for all the extra help above and beyond
in all weather and at all hours

Declan Lowney
Charlie Connelly
Carol Maddock
Gerry Hoban
John Moynes
Lenny Abrahamson
Dr Joseph Roche
Ruth McAvinia
Dr John O'Donoghue
John Ryan

Alan, Amy, Bob & Elizabeth West
And Eddie the Dog

WHAT IF?
First published in 2016 by
New Island Books
16 Priory Office Park
Stillorgan
Co. Dublin
Republic of Ireland.

www.newisland.ie

Print ISBN: 978-1-84840-560-8
Epub ISBN: 978-1-84840-561-5
Mobi ISBN: 978-1-84840-562-2

British Library Cataloguing Data.
A CIP catalogue record for this book is available from the British Library.

Typeset by Mariel Deegan
Cover Design by Mariel Deegan
Printed by

New Island received financial assistance from The Arts Council (An Chomhairle Ealaíon), 70 Merrion Square, Dublin 2, Ireland.

10 9 8 7 6 5 4 3 2 1